The Best Of
Alex
2023

Charles Peattie & Russell Taylor

Masterley Publishing

The Best Of
Alex
2023

First Published in 2024 by MASTERLEY PUBLISHING

Layout and Design: Suzette Field

Colouring and Artworking: Sofie Dodgson and Miki Lowe

ISBN: 978-1-8382562-3-4

Printed and bound by CPI Group (UK) Ltd, Croydon, CR0 4YY

FOREWORD

"Step into the realm of Alex's corporate satire, where pie charts have a sense of humor, coffee mugs attend board meetings, and the only thing sharper than the office banter is the wit on these pages! Get ready for a hilarious journey through the corporate maze with Alex - where every punchline is a promotion in the world of laughter!"

Happy reading!

Yours,

ChatGPT

PS. The book was running a bit late this year, with various illnesses and technical problems, so to avoid creating further delays we thought we'd outsource the writing of this introduction letter to AI. Half the stuff you read online these days is written by chatbots - social media posts, marketing mail outs, Amazon reviews, resumés, etc, so why should we pass up the opportunity to save a bit of time in our busy lives? We're sure that no one will have spotted the subterfuge. And if all goes well, perhaps next year we'll get AI to write and draw all the cartoons too so we can properly put our feet up.

What could possibly go wrong?

Charles Peattie and Russell Taylor

Penny

William

Clive

Rupert

Cyrus

Alex

Sasha

Christopher

Bridget

Sara

Andy

Alex
FEATTIE + TAYLOR

DAN, OUR HEAD OF DIGITAL DEVELOPMENT HAS BEEN TRYING TO CONVINCE US OF THE POTENTIAL OF THE METAVERSE AS THE FUTURE OF FINANCE.

HE AND HIS TEAM OF ENGINEERS SET UP A WHOLE FINANCIAL ECOSPHERE, WHERE INDIVIDUALS EXIST AS AVATARS AND CONDUCT TRANSACTIONS USING A NATIVE VIRTUAL CURRENCY.

WE RECENTLY HAD OUR FINGERS BURNED IN THE CRYPTOCURRENCY CRASH, BUT IT'S IMPORTANT THAT WE DON'T NEGLECT THE OPPORTUNITIES OFFERED TO US BY THIS NEW FORM OF DIGITAL FINANCE...

YES.

SO WE'VE FIRED DAN'S ENTIRE TEAM TO RECOUP SOME OF OUR COSTS...

HE'S GOING TO BE VERY CROSS WHEN HE FINALLY TAKES OFF THAT V.R. HEADSET AND NOTICES...

Alex
FEATTIE + TAYLOR

DAN IS STILL CONVINCED OF THE POTENTIAL OF THE METAVERSE IN FINANCE EVEN THOUGH WE FIRED HIS ENTIRE TEAM FOLLOWING THE TECH CRASH.

HE SAYS IT'S ONE STAGE ON FROM CRYPTO-CURRENCIES, CREATING AN ENTIRE DIGITAL REALITY POPULATED WITH INDIVIDUALS EXISTING AS AVATARS AND USING A NATIVE DIGITAL CURRENCY FOR FINANCIAL TRANSACTIONS

BUT TO BE FAIR HE'S SHOWN US SOME OF THE ADVANTAGES OF THE VIRTUAL REALM OVER TRADITIONAL BANKING PRACTICES.

YES...

WE'D HOPED TO GET HIM TO RESIGN BY STICKING HIM OUT HERE IN A ROOM ALL ON HIS OWN...

BUT LIVING IN THAT V.R. WORLD HE DOESN'T SEEM TO CARE... OR TO HAVE EVEN NOTICED...

Alex
FEATTIE + TAYLOR

WE'RE TRYING TO GET DAN, OUR HEAD OF DIGITAL, TO RESIGN AS HE'S TOO HIGHLY-PAID FOR US TO MAKE REDUNDANT.

WE'VE FIRED HIS WHOLE TEAM AND LEFT HIM SITTING IN AN OFFICE ON HIS OWN, BUT HE DOESN'T CARE AS HE SPENDS ALL HIS TIME IN THE METAVERSE AS AN AVATAR...

MAYBE WE COULD RECONSIDER.

PERHAPS WE'RE BEING HASTY IN REJECTING HIS NOTION OF A VIRTUAL REALM LIKE THIS AS A VALID FUTURE FINANCIAL ECOSYSTEM.

YOU'RE RIGHT.

WE SHOULD PAY HIS SALARY IN "MEGAS"– THE NATIVE TOKENS USED FOR TRANSACTIONS IN OUR METAVERSE...

YES... IT'S A VIRTUAL CURRENCY DIGITALLY GENERATED BY US, SO HE CAN HAVE AS MUCH OF IT AS HE LIKES...

PROBLEM SOLVED...

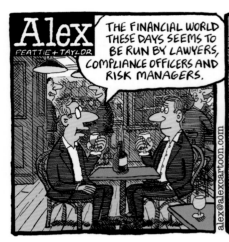
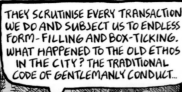

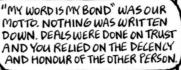

Panel 1: REMEMBER THE "GREAT RESIGNATION" THAT EVERYONE WAS TALKING ABOUT WHEN MARKETS WERE BOOMING EARLIER THIS YEAR?

Panel 2: WE'D ALL SETTLED INTO WORKING FROM HOME DURING THE PANDEMIC AND WERE THREATENING TO QUIT IF OUR BOSSES FORCED US TO COME BACK TO THE OFFICE.

YES. THEY WEREN'T VERY HAPPY ABOUT THAT...

Panel 3: BUT NOW THE ECONOMY'S COLLAPSED AND THERE'S A COST OF LIVING CRISIS AND FEWER OTHER JOBS TO GO TO, WE'VE ALL RETURNED TO THE OFFICE OUT OF SHEER FEAR, SO OUR BOSSES ARE FINALLY GETTING THEIR WISH...

YES...

Panel 4: THEY STILL DON'T LOOK HAPPY THOUGH...

DAMN. WE COULD REALLY USE A FEW OF THEM RESIGNING NOW.

YES, IT'D SAVE US HAVING TO MAKE THEM REDUNDANT AND PAY THEM OFF...

Panel 5: THE PEACE AND SECLUSION OF WORKING FROM HOME VERY MUCH SUITS FUND MANAGERS LIKE ME.

Panel 6: I NEED TO GET AWAY FROM THE DISTRACTION OF A BUSY OFFICE, SO I CAN THINK MY GREAT THOUGHTS AND MAKE MY INVESTMENT DECISIONS. AND IF I NEED TO TALK TO BROKERS LIKE YOU, THERE'S ALWAYS ZOOM CALLS...

Panel 7: WE FUND MANAGERS TEND TO LIKE THIS NEW ARRANGEMENT, AND IF YOU BROKERS DON'T IT'S PROBABLY BECAUSE YOU'RE RELUCTANT TO ACCEPT THAT THE DYNAMICS OF OUR INDUSTRY HAVE CHANGED...

Panel 8: NAMELY THAT WE'RE BETTER PAID THAN YOU THESE DAYS. I DO HOPE MY SWIMMING POOL AND TENNIS COURT ARE VISIBLE IN THE BACKGROUND...

NOW GIVE ME AN INVESTMENT IDEA SO I CAN MAKE EVEN MORE MONEY...

Panel 9: OUR BOSSES THINK THEY'VE FINALLY SUCCEEDED IN BREAKING THE WILL OF US JUNIORS AND GETTING US TO RETURN TO THE OFFICE...

Panel 10: BUT THE TRUTH IS WE'VE ONLY BEEN COMING IN OVER THE SUMMER BECAUSE THE WEATHER HAS BEEN FREAKISHLY HOT AND THE OFFICE HAS AIR CONDITIONING, UNLIKE OUR FLATS.

RIGHT.

Panel 11: BUT NOW THAT SUMMER WEATHER IS COMING TO AN END OUR PRIORITIES ARE GOING TO CHANGE...

YES.

Panel 12: AND WE'LL KEEP COMING IN BECAUSE WE WON'T BE ABLE TO AFFORD TO HEAT OUR FLATS IN THE WINTER WITH THE MASSIVE RISE IN ENERGY PRICES.

HMM. SO HOW ARE WE GOING TO SHOW OUR BOSSES THAT WE'RE STILL REBELS?

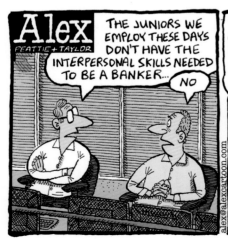

Alex PEATTIE + TAYLOR

I HEAR THAT OUR BANK HAS DRAWN UP CONTINGENCY PLANS TO RELOCATE STAFF BACK TO LONDON FROM FRANKFURT.

THAT'S RIGHT.

NOW THAT THE RUSSIANS HAVE CUT OFF THE NORDSTREAM GAS PIPELINE TO GERMANY THERE ARE FEARS THAT THERE COULD BE POWER OUTAGES OR EVEN ENERGY RATIONING THERE IN THE WINTER.

OBVIOUSLY THE POSSIBILITY OF BEING WITHOUT A RELIABLE ELECTRICITY SUPPLY COULD SERIOUSLY IMPACT ON THE ABILITY OF BANKERS TO FUNCTION OUT THERE.

YES.

THEY WOULDN'T BE ABLE TO WATCH NETFLIX IN THEIR APARTMENTS IN THE LONG TEDIOUS EVENINGS.

THERE'S NOTHING ELSE TO DO IN FRANKFURT. IT'S THE ONLY THING THAT KEEPS THEM SANE.

Alex PEATTIE + TAYLOR

PUTIN HAS SUCCESS-FULLY REVIVED RUSSIA'S SOVIET-ERA ANIMOSITY TOWARDS THE BOURGEOIS WEST.

HE'S MOVED ON FROM MILITARY CONFLICT IN UKRAINE TO WAGING FULL-ON ECONOMIC WAR AGAINST EUROPE BY WITHOLDING GAS AND OIL SUPPLIES, BUT IN A SITUATION LIKE THIS WE MUST HOLD FIRM TO OUR PRINCIPLES.

WE MAY BE CONSIDERED SOFT AND DECADENT BUT WE NEED TO STAND UP FOR OUR RIGHTS AND FREEDOMS AND VIGOROUSLY OPPOSE THOSE WHO SEEK TO CONTROL AND DICTATE TO US...

OUR BOSSES AT THE BANK WHO ARE TRYING TO GET US TO GO BACK TO THE OFFICE?

AND WITH DOMESTIC HEATING BILLS SET TO SKY-ROCKET IT'S VERY TEMPTING...

RESIST! WE WILL FREEZE AT HOME RATHER THAN SUBMIT TO THEIR WILL.

Alex PEATTIE + TAYLOR

PUTIN'S CLOSING THE GAS PIPELINES TO EUROPE AS PART OF HIS ECONOMIC WAR AGAINST THE WEST MAY NOT BE AS EFFECTIVE AS HE SUPPOSES.

TRUE, INSTITUTIONS LIKE BANKS RELY ON A CONTINUOUS SUPPLY OF POWER AND ANY INTERRUPTIONS WOULD ORDINARILY BE DANGEROUS, BUT THESE DAYS MOST OF OUR STAFF CAN WORK FROM HOME AND THUS THE PROBLEM CAN BE MITIGATED.

SO THE REVOLUTION IN HOME WORKING MEANS THAT EVEN IF THERE WAS A MAJOR POWER OUTAGE IN THE BANK'S CITY HQ WE WOULD BE PROTECTED AGAINST THE DIRE CONSEQUENCES...

WHAT, OF US HAVING TO GO AND WORK IN CROYDON?

QUITE. HOPEFULLY THE BANK WON'T NEED ITS DISASTER RECOVERY SITE OUT IN THE SUBURBS ANY MORE...

Alex PEATTIE + TAYLOR

SO YOU'RE NO LONGER HOSTILE TO EMPLOYEES WORKING FROM HOME, CYRUS?

NO, I'VE REALIZED IT CAN BE USEFUL FOR THE BANK...

IN THIS INFLATIONARY ENVIRONMENT PEOPLE ARE DEMANDING PAY RISES, BUT THERE'S A RECESSION LOOMING AND WE'VE NO MONEY TO PAY THEM, SO WE'RE OFFERING THEM EXTRA DAYS A WEEK WORKING FROM HOME AS A TRADE-OFF.

THEY SAVE TIME AND MONEY BY NOT COMMUTING AND WE CAN SPEND LESS ON DESKS, COMPUTERS ETC...

SO EVERYONE'S HAPPY?

EXCEPT FOR PATRICK THERE, WHO BOUGHT AN EXPENSIVE DOCKLANDS APARTMENT TEN YEARS AGO TO BE "CLOSE TO WORK"...

WFH DOESN'T SAVE HIM ANY TIME OR MONEY AS HE LIVES A FIVE MINUTE WALK FROM THE BANK...

NO WONDER HE'S CROSS...

Alex PEATTIE + TAYLOR

I WASN'T SURE WHETHER I WANTED TO REMAIN IN POLITICS BEFORE THIS WEEK, CLIVE.

GOVERNMENT POLICY JUST SEEMED TO BE STUCK IN THIS NEO-LIBERAL REDISTRIBUTIONIST FUDGE... IT WAS QUITE DEPRESSING...

BUT NOW MY GOVERNMENT HAS BROUGHT IN THIS AMAZING THATCHERITE LOW-TAX, HIGH-BONUS BUDGET... AND AS A BACK BENCHER I FEEL A RENEWED SENSE OF PURPOSE...

REALLY?

YES, TO BAIL OUT OF POLITICS AND GET BACK TO MAKING REAL MONEY IN THE CITY WHILE THE GOING IS GOOD... I'M PHONING MY HEADHUNTER NOW...

I RECKON THERE'S A COUPLE OF YEARS FOR ME TO TOP UP MY PENSION BEFORE IT ALL GOES T*TS-UP AND LABOUR GETS IN...

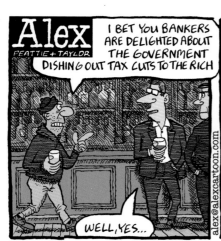

Alex PEATTIE + TAYLOR

I BET YOU BANKERS ARE DELIGHTED ABOUT THE GOVERNMENT DISHING OUT TAX CUTS TO THE RICH

WELL, YES...

BUT ACTUALLY THE POINT OF LAST WEEK'S MINI BUDGET WAS TO SEND OUT A SIGNAL THAT BRITAIN IS OPEN FOR BUSINESS, WHICH WILL ATTRACT MORE PEOPLE TO COME AND WORK HERE.

OH YEH? MORE BANKERS LIKE YOU, NO DOUBT...

IT'S TRUE THAT LONDON WILL NOW BE A DESIRABLE BASE FOR AMERICAN AND EUROPEAN INVESTMENT BANKS, THANKS TO THE PRIME BUSINESS CONDITIONS THAT THE CHANCELLOR HAS CREATED...

BY REMOVING THE CAP ON BANKERS' BONUSES?

ER, NO...

BY COLLAPSING STERLING ON INTERNATIONAL CURRENCY MARKETS,

WHICH WILL BENEFIT THOSE OF US WORKING OVER HERE WHOSE SALARY IS PAID IN DOLLARS OR EUROS...

WHICH I SUSPECT YOURS ISN'T...

alex@alexcartoon.com

15

Alex PEATTIE + TAYLOR

HANDING OUT TAX CUTS TO THE RICH? REMOVING THE CAP ON BANKERS' BONUSES? THIS GOVERNMENT IS A TOTAL DISGRACE...

IT HAS NO MANDATE FOR THESE IRRESPONSIBLE, OPPORTUNISTIC POLICIES, WHICH ONLY BENEFIT THE WEALTHIEST 1% OF SOCIETY, INCLUDING BANKERS LIKE YOU AND WHICH PUT THE NATION'S FINANCES AT RISK...

I AGREE...

I THINK IT'S AN ILL-THOUGHT-OUT AND ECONOMICALLY POTENTIALLY DISASTROUS POLICY DECISION AND I'VE MADE MY DISAPPROVAL OF IT VERY CLEAR...

OH. GOOD.

BY SELLING THE HECK OUT OF STERLING... I'VE MADE A FORTUNE.

ME TOO. OUR BONUSES WILL BE HUGE THIS YEAR.

GRRR...

AND LUCKILY NO ONE'S GOING TO CAP THEM...

Alex PEATTIE + TAYLOR

WELL THE GOVERNMENT'S POLICY IS PUSHING UP INTEREST RATES WHICH MEANS MORTGAGES GOING UP NOW TOO...

YES

THIS WILL PUT THE PROSPECT OF EVER GETTING ON THE HOUSING LADDER EVEN FURTHER OUT OF REACH FOR OUR DISILLUSIONED MILLENNIUM GENERATION EMPLOYEES...

SO THE GOVERNMENT HAS DELIVERED ANOTHER CRUSHING BLOW TO OUR YOUNGSTERS LEAVING THEM WITHOUT THE OPTION WHICH AT ONE TIME THEY THOUGHT THEY'D BE ABLE TO TAKE FOR GRANTED...

YES.

BECAUSE OF THE EXCHANGE RATE, THEY CAN'T EVEN AFFORD TO GO OFF ABROAD ON ANOTHER 'GAP YEAR' LIKE THEY USUALLY THREATEN TO DO WHEN THEY'RE A BIT P*SSED OFF AT WORK

MEANING WE DON'T EVEN NEED TO PAY THEM EXTRA TO RETAIN THEM. HOORAY!

Alex PEATTIE + TAYLOR

THERE'S A NEW TREND OF "QUIET QUITTING" AMONG YOUNGER EMPLOYEES IN THE CORPORATE WORLD.

THEY'RE DISILLUSIONED WITH WORK AND REFUSE TO DO MORE THAN THE BARE MINIMUM. IT'S EVEN AFFECTED MEMBERS OF OUR DEPARTMENT...

WELL, WE NEED TO PUT A STOP TO THIS. OUR PEOPLE SHOULD TAKE A PRIDE IN THEIR JOBS AND BE WORKING HARD.

IMAGINE WHAT THE SENIOR DIRECTORS OF THE BANK WOULD THINK IF THEY HEARD OUR DEPARTMENT WAS ON A DELIBERATE WORK GO-SLOW...

YES...

THEY'D BE VERY VERY HAPPY.

EXACTLY. AND WE DON'T WANT THAT. OUR MISSION HERE IN COMPLIANCE IS TO BE A PERMANENT PAIN IN THE A*SE TO THEM...

17

20

21

Alex FEATTIE + TAYLOR

I SURE PICKED A HELL OF A TIME TO GO ON HONEYMOON, SASHA.

2022 WAS ALREADY BAD FOR BUSINESS WITH THE WAR IN UKRAINE, INFLATION AND THE TECH CRASH, BUT THE DISASTROUS SHORT-LIVED LIZ TRUSS PREMIERSHIP FURTHER DESTABILIZED MARKETS AND DESTROYED INVESTOR CONFIDENCE.

NOT ONLY WAS I AWAY FROM MY DESK FOR THOSE CRUCIAL WEEKS BUT I WAS ALSO ON MY ANNUAL CORE LEAVE, MEANING I WASN'T ALLOWED TO CONTACT MY CLIENTS OR ANY OF MY CO-WORKERS AT THE BANK...

SO I CAN BLAME ALL THE DEALS THAT FAILED TO HAPPEN ON MY NUMBER TWO WHO I LEFT IN CHARGE IN MY ABSENCE.

THAT'LL BE CLIVE THEN?

IT'S ALWAYS GOOD TO HAVE AN EXCUSE TO DOWNGRADE HIS BONUS.

Alex FEATTIE + TAYLOR

ACCORDING TO A SURVEY 70% OF YOUNG PEOPLE IN THE CORPORATE WORLD INTEND TO LEAVE THEIR JOB IN THE NEXT YEAR IN ORDER TO DO SOMETHING MORE WORTHWHILE

IT'S LINKED IN WITH THIS NEW TREND FOR "QUIET QUITTING" AMONG YOUNGER EMPLOYEES, IT MEANS THEY JUST DO THE MINIMUM OF WORK REQUIRED OF THEM.

WELL, EACH YEAR THE BANK GETS RID OF THE BOTTOM 10% PERFORMERS.

SO CLEARLY THESE ARE THE PEOPLE THAT WE'RE GOING TO TARGET.

BUT WON'T IT MAKE THEM HAPPY IF THEY GET MADE REDUNDANT AND GIVEN A PAY-OFF?

WELL, YES...

BUT THINK HOW ANNOYED ALL THE REST OF THEM WHO DON'T GET MADE REDUNDANT ARE GOING TO BE...

OH YES! I LIKE IT...

Alex FEATTIE + TAYLOR

IT'S BEEN A BAD YEAR FOR TECH COMPANIES AND NOW META AND AMAZON HAVE SEEN FURTHER REVERSALS IN THEIR SHARE PRICES.

IT COMES AS NO SURPRISE TO THOSE OF US WHO REMEMBER MARCH 2000 WHEN OVERHYPED, OVERVALUED DOTCOM COMPANIES CAME CRASHING BACK TO EARTH, BUT IT MUST BE A REAL SHOCK TO OUR YOUNGER COLLEAGUES.

THEY'RE THE GENERATION WHO GREW UP WITH SOCIAL MEDIA AND SMART-PHONES. FOR THEM TECHNOLOGY IS CENTRAL TO THEIR EXISTENCE, THEIR RATIONALE, THEIR LIFESTYLE CHOICES.

SUCH AS THEM ALL WANTING TO "QUIET QUIT" THEIR JOBS?

EXACTLY. LET'S SEE IF THEY'RE QUITE SO KEEN TO FLOUNCE OUT NOW THAT THERE ARE NO HIGH-PAYING TECH ROLES FOR THEM TO GO TO.

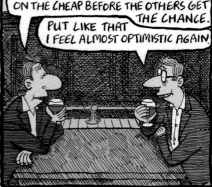

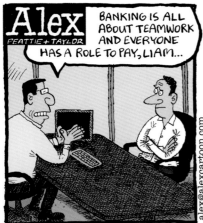

Alex PEATTIE + TAYLOR

ALEX MASTERLEY IS STARTING HIS OWN FINANCIAL BOUTIQUE. HE SAYS IT'S THE FUTURE FOR OUR INDUSTRY.

IT'S TRUE...

WE'RE SEEING A MOVE IN THE CITY BACK TOWARDS SMALL, FOCUSED BUSINESSES...THERE'S A FEELING THAT THE BIG INVESTMENT BANKS HAVE BECOME TOO DIVERSIFIED IN THEIR BUSINESS MODEL...

THAT WAS THE PROBLEM WHEN ALEX USED TO WORK AT MEGABANK; WHEN AS A CLIENT, YOU ASKED HIM ABOUT STUFF, HE'D INVARIABLY HAVE TO ADMIT THAT IT WASN'T HIS AREA OF SPECIALITY...

TRUE...

I NEVER ACTUALLY FOUND OUT WHAT HIS AREA OF SPECIALITY *WAS*...

PERHAPS NOW WE WILL...

SOMEHOW I DOUBT IT...

Alex PEATTIE + TAYLOR

ALEX MASTERLEY HAS ALWAYS BEEN CONVINCED THAT CLIENTS DEALT WITH HIM BECAUSE OF HIS PERSONAL REPUTATION.

WHEREAS HIS EX-EMPLOYER MEGABANK, LIKE ALL BIG BANKS, REMAINS CONVINCED THAT IT'S THE KUDOS OF ITS NAME THAT BRINGS THE CLIENTS THROUGH THE DOOR...

NOW ALEX IS STARTING HIS OWN FINANCIAL BOUTIQUE HE'LL HAVE A KEEN AWARENESS OF HOW IMPORTANT HIS NAME IS TO BRINGING IN THE BUSINESS...

HOW ABOUT "MASTERLEY CAPITAL" AS YOUR COMPANY NAME?

NO WAY. IT'LL JUST MEAN THAT ALL CLIENTS WILL ALWAYS INSIST ON SEEING *ME* AND I'LL NEVER BE ABLE TO DELEGATE ANY WORK TO MY SUBORDINATES.

Alex PEATTIE + TAYLOR

FOR YEARS WE IN THE FINANCIAL WORLD WERE IN THRALL TO THE TECH SECTOR...

YES, WE WERE TOO FEARFUL OF MISSING OUT ON THE BOOM.

SO DESPITE OUR MISGIVINGS, WE SAID POSITIVE THINGS ABOUT COMPANIES WHICH OFTEN MADE NO PROFIT, WHOSE WORTH WAS BASED ON DUBIOUS CRYPTOCURRENCIES AND WHICH WERE CLEARLY HUGELY OVERSTAFFED

BUT NOW THAT THE TECH MARKET HAS CRASHED THAT'S ALL CHANGED AND WE FIND OURSELVES FIRMLY BACK IN CONTROL AND ABLE TO PROPERLY EXERCISE OUR JUDGEMENT AS CITY ANALYSTS...

YES...

AND WE NOW HAVE TO WORK OUT WHICH TECH COMPANIES ARE ACTUALLY GOOD INVESTMENTS. INSTEAD OF JUST WRITING A BLANKET BUY RECOMMENDATION ON THE WHOLE SECTOR...

≡SIGH≡ I MISS THOSE TIMES...THINGS WERE SO EASY...

Alex PEATTIE + TAYLOR

SO IT'S BEEN DECIDED: WE'VE ALL BEEN MUCH TOO SOFT ON EMPLOYEES WHO WFH. IT'S TIME FOR A NEW WORKING ETHOS TO BE CREATED.

RIGHT.

WE PLAN TO INSTITUTE A RETURN TO 1990S STYLE 70-HOUR WORKING WEEKS WITH ALL OUR SNOWFLAKE JUNIORS COMING INTO THE OFFICE FULL-TIME.

HMM...

I CAN'T HELP WORRYING THAT THE IMPLICATIONS OF IMPLEMENTING THIS REGIME HAVEN'T BEEN FULLY THOUGHT THROUGH...

WHAT? LIKE HOW?

WELL, WON'T IT MEAN ALL OF US BOSSES WILL HAVE TO COME IN OURSELVES TOO, TO ENFORCE IT?

WHAT?!! OH NO! I WFH 3 DAYS A WEEK...

AND I LIVE IN SUFFOLK NOW...

OOPS. YES, AND I WAS ONLY PLANNING TO COME IN ONE DAY THIS MONTH MYSELF: TODAY...

Alex PEATTIE + TAYLOR

THIS WORLD CUP HAS PRODUCED SOME UNEXPECTED RESULTS, WITH STRONG SHOWINGS FROM THE AFRICAN AND ASIAN TEAMS.

YES.

IT SEEMS THE TRADITIONAL DOMINANCE OF EUROPEAN AND SOUTH AMERICAN COUNTRIES MAY HAVE BEEN BROKEN, WITH UNDER-DOGS LIKE SAUDI ARABIA, MOROCCO AND JAPAN PULLING OFF SHOCK WINS AGAINST SUPPOSEDLY SUPERIOR OPPOSITION.

OF COURSE IT COMES AS NO SURPRISE TO MANY OF US. AFTER ALL, THE WORLD IS RAPIDLY CHANGING FROM THE OLD ESTABLISHED ORDER...

YES, IT IS...

AND WE NOW GET TO WORK FROM HOME A LOT, SO WE'RE ABLE TO WATCH THE DAYTIME MATCHES FEATURING THE MAKEWEIGHT TEAMS THAT WE WOULDN'T NORMALLY SEE...

WELL IT HELPS WHILE AWAY THE TIME...

Alex PEATTIE + TAYLOR

I'M EXCITED ABOUT JOINING YOUR FINANCIAL BOUTIQUE, ALEX, BUT IS THIS THE RIGHT TIME TO BE STARTING A NEW BUSINESS?

THE STOCK MARKET BOOM OF THE LAST FEW YEARS SEEMS TO BE OVER AND WE'RE FACING A DOWNTURN AND A POSSIBLE RECESSION.

YES.

WHICH MAKES IT THE PERFECT TIME TO START THIS BUSINESS... BECAUSE ANYONE CAN MAKE MONEY IN A BULL MARKET, BUT IT TAKES TALENT TO MAKE IT IN A BEAR MARKET?

ER, NO...

BECAUSE PREVIOUSLY I'D HAVE HAD TO OFFER YOU A BIG SALARY TO LURE YOU AWAY FROM YOUR BANK, BUT SINCE YOU WERE MADE REDUNDANT DUE TO THE DOWNTURN, I WAS ABLE TO HIRE YOU ON A COMMISSION-ONLY BASIS.

AH, YES...

30

Alex PEATTIE + TAYLOR

WHEN I STARTED IN THE CITY EVERYONE WORE A SUIT AND TIE. IT WAS DE RIGUEUR...

BUT THEN THIS AWFUL NEW DRESS ETHOS CREPT IN WHEREBY PEOPLE WOULD WEAR A SUIT AND AN OPEN-NECK SHIRT AND ONLY PUT ON A TIE IF THEY HAD A CLIENT MEETING...

IT'S GOT WORSE SINCE YOU RETIRED, RUPERT.

NOWADAYS PEOPLE DRESS TOTALLY CASUALLY AND DON'T EVEN BOTHER TO WEAR A JACKET UNLESS THEY'VE GOT A CLIENT MEETING...

WHAT, NO JACKETS?

SO WHAT DO THEY HANG ON THE BACK OF THEIR CHAIR WHEN THEY'RE OUT TO LUNCH TO MAKE IT LOOK LIKE THEY'RE STILL IN THE BUILDING?

NO ONE GOES TO LUNCH...

OR COMES INTO THE BUILDING MUCH..

I'M WELL OUT OF THAT WORLD...

Alex PEATTIE + TAYLOR

NIKKI, AS MY P.A. I DO NEED YOU TO COME INTO THE OFFICE SOMETIMES...

WHY?

I CAN HANDLE ALL YOUR ARRANGEMENTS, MEETINGS AND BUSINESS REMOTELY, AND LIAISE WITH YOU FROM MY HOME ON VIDEO LIKE THIS...

YES, BUT...

AND THE ONLY REASON YOU'RE EVER IN TOWN NOWADAYS IS ABOUT TWICE A MONTH FOR AN INTERNAL MEETING WITH SOMEONE ELSE FROM THE BANK. WHAT'S THE POINT OF ME BEING THERE TOO?

TO KEEP THEM WAITING FOR ME OUTSIDE MY OFFICE FOR A PERIOD OF TIME, TO REMIND THEM HOW IMPORTANT I AM.

WELL, IT'LL HAVE TO FIT IN ROUND MY SCHOOL RUNS ETC...

IT'S YOUR JOB TO MAKE THAT HAPPEN.

Alex PEATTIE + TAYLOR

EVEN THE MOST DIEHARD BREXITEER LIKE YOURSELF MUST BE STARTING TO THINK THAT LEAVING THE EU WAS A MISTAKE, CLIVE...

I'M RELUCTANTLY INCLINED TO AGREE...

BREXIT MIGHT EVEN PRECIPITATE THE BREAK-UP OF THE UK, WITH SCOTLAND USING THE EXCUSE TO HOLD ANOTHER REFERENDUM, GAINING INDEPENDENCE AND THEN JOINING THE EUROPEAN UNION.

COULD THAT HAPPEN, ALEX?

I MEAN, ENGLAND AND SCOTLAND HAVE BEEN SO INTERTWINED SOCIALLY AND CULTURALLY FOR CENTURIES. IN ANY CASE HOW WOULD AN INDEPENDENT SCOTLAND SURVIVE ECONOMICALLY?

BY SELLING SCOTTISH EU PASSPORTS AT EXTORTIONATE RATES TO ENGLISH PEOPLE WITH SCOTTISH GRANDPARENTS.

HMM... I'VE ALWAYS QUITE FANCIED THE IDEA OF BEING ABLE TO RETIRE TO FRANCE IF THINGS WENT T*TS-UP HERE...

Alex FEATTIE + TAYLOR

WHEN I HEAR YOUR STORIES OF THE OLD DAYS OF THE CITY I CAN'T BELIEVE WHAT YOU GUYS GOT UP TO...

YOU'D SPEND HALF YOUR TIME ON GROUSE MOORS OR AT GLYNDBOURNE OR COWES AND IT WAS CONSIDERED PART OF YOUR JOB...

WE WERE ENTERTAINING, DEAR BOY.

WELL, THAT'S SOMETHING I'LL NEVER GET TO DO AND WHAT'S WORSE, YOU BABY BOOMERS ARE NOW RETIRING ON GENEROUS FINAL SALARY PENSIONS, WHICH IS SOMETHING ELSE MY GENERATION WILL NEVER GET...

BUT WE NEED THEM. YES.

TO FUND THE EXPENSIVE HOBBIES WE'VE ACQUIRED OVER OUR WORKING LIVES.

EXACTLY, SHOOTING OPERA AND SAILING DON'T COME CHEAP, YOU KNOW.

Alex FEATTIE + TAYLOR

SO YOU'RE DRAWING UP THE NEW YEAR REDUNDANCY LIST, CYRUS?

YES, AND CLIVE'S NAME IS AT THE TOP OF IT...

HE'S ONLY KEPT HIS JOB BECAUSE I NEEDED HIM TO PAY BRIDGET'S MAINTENANCE, BUT NOW THAT I'M MARRIED TO HER THAT NO LONGER APPLIES.

OBVIOUSLY IT WOULD GIVE ME GREAT PERSONAL PLEASURE TO IMPOSE MAXIMUM HUMILIATION ON HIM, BUT CAN I REALLY IN ALL CONSCIENCE NOW JUST FIRE HIM?

WHAT, BECAUSE PEOPLE WHO LOSE THEIR JOBS IN THE FIRST WAVE CAN OFTEN FIND NEW ONES QUITE EASILY?

EXACTLY, BUT IN A MONTH OR 2, THERE'LL BE MORE COMPETITION...

BUT IF I DELAY FIRING HIM IT MIGHT SUGGEST THAT I DIDN'T THINK HE WAS UTTERLY USELESS...

IT'S A DILEMMA.

Alex FEATTIE + TAYLOR

THE DRESS CODE IN A CITY OFFICE HAS CHANGED UNRECOGNISABLY OVER THE YEARS.

ONCE UPON A TIME WE WERE ALL OBLIGED TO CONFORM TO THE FORMAL IMAGE OF WHAT A BANKER SHOULD LOOK LIKE AND HAD TO DON THE STANDARD UNIFORM OF SUIT AND TIE EVERY DAY OF THE WEEK.

BUT NOWADAYS THERE'S MUCH MORE FLEXIBILITY IN WHAT ONE CAN WEAR, WHICH ALLOWS PEOPLE TO USE HOW THEY DRESS TO MAKE A PERSONAL STATEMENT.

YES.

OH NO... THE BOSS IS IN A SUIT TODAY... EITHER HE'S GOT AN IMPORTANT CLIENT MEETING OR HE'S GOING TO FIRE PEOPLE...

WELL JUDGING BY OUR CURRENT DEARTH OF DEALS I KNOW WHAT MY MONEY IS ON

OO-ER...

THIS IS THE BLEAKEST START TO A NEW YEAR THAT I CAN REMEMBER...

2022 WAS AN UNMITIGATED DISASTER FOR BUSINESS AND A RECESSION IS NOW INEVITABLE. NO ONE IS EXPECTING A BONUS AND MOST ARE FEARFUL OF BEING MADE REDUNDANT.

OF COURSE THIS IS THE TIME WHERE PEOPLE TRADITIONALLY RENEW THEIR SEASON TICKETS. IT'S INTERESTING TO SEE WHO'S SO CONFIDENT OF THEIR FUTURE EMPLOYMENT PROSPECTS THAT THEY RENEW THEIRS...

LOOK, I'VE BOUGHT ONE OF THESE NEW "FLEXI" SEASON TICKETS WHICH LETS ME TRAVEL ON UP TO EIGHT DAYS IN ANY ONE MONTH.

NOT ONLY DOES HE THINK WE'LL STILL BE EMPLOYING HIM, BUT ALSO THAT WE'LL BE ALLOWING HIM TO WORK FROM HOME...

THE DELUDED FOOL...

2022 WAS A DISASTROUS YEAR, SO BEFORE SETTING THE BUDGETS FOR 2023 I'VE ASKED MY TEAM FOR THEIR OUTLOOK ON THE YEAR AHEAD.

SO IF PEOPLE ARE PESSIMISTIC ABOUT BUSINESS LEVELS IT MEANS THEY DON'T THINK THERE'LL BE MUCH WORK TO DO THIS YEAR SO THEY WON'T EXPECT ME TO MAKE AN EFFORT TO RETAIN THEM IN THEIR JOBS BY PAYING THEM GENEROUS BONUSES.

BUT IF THEY'RE TOO OPTIMISTIC ABOUT THE COMING YEAR THEY RISK ME SETTING THEIR TARGETS SO HIGH THAT THEY'LL FAIL TO MEET THEM AND WILL GET FIRED...

RIGHT. SO WHAT'S THE OVERALL CONSENSUS?

EVERYONE'S BEING VAGUE, CAUTIOUS, WOOLLY AND NON-COMMITTAL.

WHICH IS NOT AN ATTITUDE THAT'S LIKELY TO EARN THEM A BONUS...

EXACTLY. IT ALL HELPS KEEP COSTS DOWN...

WE'LL NEED A "VISION" FOR THIS FINANCIAL BOUTIQUE WE'RE SETTING UP. WHAT ARE OUR "CORE VALUES"?

INTEGRITY...? TRUST...? FAIRNESS...?

HEY, GUYS, CAN'T WE JUST BE HONEST AND SAY "MAKING MONEY"? IT'S OUR COMPANY AFTER ALL AND WE HAVEN'T GOT TO PANDER TO ALL THAT POLITICALLY CORRECT CORPORATE NONSENSE ANY MORE.

I DISAGREE, PAUL. IN ORDER TO SUCCEED AS A BUSINESS IT'S IMPORTANT TO SHOW THAT WE ESPOUSE HIGHER VALUES...

YES INDEED...

ABSTRACT AND INTANGIBLE ONES THAT IT'S HARD FOR ANYONE TO SAY FOR SURE THAT WE FAILED TO DELIVER...

"MAKING MONEY" IS MUCH TOO EASILY VERIFIABLE.

FAIR ENOUGH.

Alex PEATTIE + TAYLOR

I'VE JUST GOT BACK FROM YOGA TO FIND THE KIDS ALL ON THEIR iPADS AND VR HEADSETS

GONE ARE THE DAYS WHEN THEY MIGHT GO OUT AND PLAY FOOTBALL IN THE PARK OR EVEN DO SOME DRAWING OR CRAFTS ON A SATURDAY MORNING... NO, NOW IT'S ALL MINECRAFT OR ROBLOX OR GORILLA TAG.

SO INSTEAD OF THEM DOING SOMETHING USEFUL AT WEEKENDS, NEW TECHNOLOGY MEANS A WHOLE GENERATION CAN NOW IMMERSE ITSELF IN CHILDHOOD PLAY ACTIVITIES WHICH ARE TOTALLY FRIVOLOUS AND POINTLESS...

WHO, YOUR CHILDREN?

ER, NO...

HEY. YOU WERE SUPPOSED TO BE IN CHARGE OF THE KIDS WHILE I WAS OUT.

WELL THEY SEEMED TO BE ENTERTAINING THEMSELVES...

DAD'S MAN CAVE

SCALEXTRIC

Alex PEATTIE + TAYLOR

IT'S SHOCKING HOW WIDE THE COMMUNICATION GAP IS BETWEEN US OLDIES AND THE MILLENNIALS IN THE OFFICE.

CLIVE JUST MADE AN ALLUSION TO 1970s POP MUSIC AND IT DREW BLANK STARES FROM THE JUNIORS. HE'S HAVING TO PAINSTAKINGLY EXPLAIN THE REFERENCE TO THEM.

IT'S FUNNY TO THINK HOW A CULTURAL PHENOMENON THAT WAS SO MEANINGFUL TO HIS GENERATION CAN TOTALLY LACK ANY SIGNIFICANCE FOR YOUNGER PEOPLE.

NO, OF COURSE I'VE HEARD OF LEO SAYER. BUT THESE STORIES ABOUT CITY LUNCHES IN THE OLD DAYS... ER..?

WELL, "LEO SAYER" WAS COCKNEY RHYMING SLANG FOR AN "ALL DAYER"

YOU GUYS USED TO SPEND THE WHOLE DAY AT LUNCH?

SIGH HOW DO I EXPLAIN?

Alex PEATTIE + TAYLOR

IT TURNS OUT OUR INTERN OLIVER USED A CHATBOT TO WRITE HIS REPORT...

WHAT, THE ONE YOU GAVE HIM TO WRITE JUST TO KEEP HIM BUSY?

YES, HE WAS OVERHEARD CONFESSING TO A CO-WORKER. APPARENTLY CHATGPT PRODUCED THIS 5,000-WORD DOCUMENT WITH CHARTS AND GRAPHS IN JUST A FEW SECONDS...

TAP

AI IS SO AMAZING THESE DAYS...

BUT IS IT ACTUALLY INTELLIGENT? OKAY, IT CAN CHURN OUT PERFECT TEXT BUT WILL IT EVER BECOME SENTIENT? WILL IT BE ABLE TO UNDERSTAND COMPLEX CONCEPTS LIKE ITS OWN EXISTENCE?

LET'S HOPE NOT

OR IT'D REALISE HOW UTTERLY FUTILE IT IS...

I WAS NEVER PLANNING TO READ THIS REPORT THAT OLIVER DIDN'T ACTUALLY WRITE.

DUMP

41

Alex PEATTIE + TAYLOR

HEY, SASHA, IT'S CYRUS...

CYRUS, YOU REALLY DON'T NEED TO KEEP PHONING...

YOU'RE SUPPOSED TO BE HAVING A VALENTINE'S MINI-BREAK IN PARIS WITH YOUR WIFE. JUST CHILL, BE HAPPY AND FORGET ABOUT THE OFFICE FOR A WHILE...

I CAN'T RELAX, SASHA. I'VE BEEN AWAY FOR TWO WHOLE DAYS...

CYRUS, ALL YOU NEED TO KNOW IS THAT IT'S VERY QUIET HERE AND THERE'S NO URGENT BUSINESS OR MEETINGS THAT REQUIRE YOUR ATTENTION...

OH GOOD.

SO NONE OF MY TEAM HAS COME IN TO RESIGN AFTER GETTING THEIR BONUSES?

NOPE. OBVIOUSLY NONE OF THEM HAD NEW JOBS TO GO TO.

HA! I GOT AWAY WITH PAYING THEM ALL DONUTS... NOW I'M HAPPY...

Alex PEATTIE + TAYLOR

THE NEW UNOFFICIAL 3-DAY WORKING WEEK IN THE CITY IS HAVING A KNOCK-ON EFFECT ON THE RESTAURANT TRADE...

MONDAY WAS ALWAYS A QUIET DAY FOR LUNCHES, BUT MANY RESTAURANTS ARE NOW NOT BOTHERING TO OPEN AT ALL ON A MONDAY, AS SO MANY PEOPLE WORK FROM HOME ON THAT DAY.

IT'S A GREAT SHAME, CLIVE.

I AM A FIRM BELIEVER IN THE TRADITIONAL FIVE-DAY-A-WEEK LUNCHING SCHEDULE AND MONDAYS HAVE ALWAYS BEEN AN INDISPENSABLE PART OF THAT.

YES...

IT'S THE DAY YOU COULD INVITE YOUR WORST CLIENT TO LUNCH. PREFERABLY FOR AN HOUR-LONG SLOT AT 12-00...

EXACTLY TO HINT TO THEM THAT THEY WERE A WASTE OF YOUR VALUABLE TIME.

HOW DO WE DO THAT NOW?

Alex PEATTIE + TAYLOR

THE COMPANY I RUN IS LOOKING FOR NEW BROKERS AND YOU NOW HAVE YOUR OWN FINANCIAL BOUTIQUE, ALEX...

OBVIOUSLY AS YOU'RE AN OLD MATE I'D BE TEMPTED TO JUST GIVE MY BUSINESS TO YOU, BUT I THINK WE SHOULD DO THINGS BY THE BOOK HERE...

SO I'LL ORGANISE A "BEAUTY PARADE" AND INVITE VARIOUS OTHER CITY BROKERS TO COME IN AND PITCH FOR MY ACCOUNT. I THINK THAT'S ONLY RIGHT AND PROPER.

AGREED.

THEN I'LL JUST PINCH ALL THEIR BEST IDEAS AND GIVE MY BUSINESS TO YOU AS PLANNED.

CHEERS. THAT'LL SAVE US HAVING TO BOTHER TO THINK OF ANY IDEAS OF OUR OWN...

CLINK

44

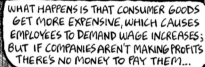

48

Alex PEATTIE + TAYLOR

THE BIG SHAKE-OUT IN THE TECH INDUSTRY MUST HAVE COME AS A SHOCK FOR MANY GENERATION Z KIDS...

THEY'VE GONE FROM HAVING CUSHY JOBS IN TECH COMPANIES WHERE THEY WERE PAMPERED AND OVERPAID, TO SUDDENLY HAVING TO FACE UP TO THE STARK REALITY OF UNEMPLOYMENT.

BUT IT'S A LOT EASIER FOR THEM THAN IT WOULD BE FOR OUR GENERATION, CLIVE.

THEY CAN JUST SLING ON A BACKPACK AND HEAD OFF TO GO TRAVELLING AROUND ASIA FOR SIX MONTHS...

TRUE...

WHERE THEY CAN CLAIM THEY'RE A "DIGITAL NOMAD" WHO'S ABLE TO USE THEIR LAPTOP TO WORK FROM ANYWHERE IN THE WORLD...

QUITE. IT'S ANNOYING THAT IT'S SO EASY FOR THEM TO AVOID LOOKING LIKE JOBLESS LOSERS...

Alex PEATTIE + TAYLOR

THE RAIL UNIONS HAVE ARRANGED THEIR STRIKE DAYS NEXT WEEK TO CAUSE MAXIMUM DISRUPTION TO PEOPLE'S WORKING LIVES...

WHAT'S THEIR GRIEVANCE?

OH, IT'S THE USUAL: PAY. BUT THE RAIL COMPANIES MANAGEMENT IS CLAIMING THERE'S NO MONEY AND IS INSISTING ON IMPOSING MODERN WORKING CONDITIONS AS A CONDITION OF ANY WAGE INCREASES, IT'S LED TO AN IMPASSE.

RIGHT.

IT'S A CLASSIC SITUATION WHERE A BUNCH OF DELUDED AND ENTITLED WORKERS THINK THEY CAN JUST IGNORE ECONOMIC REALITY AND THE DEMANDS OF THEIR BOSSES.

WHAT, OUR WORKERS?

EXACTLY

THE STRIKES NEXT WEEK WILL BE VERY DISRUPTIVE. I THINK I'LL JUST WORK FROM HOME EVERY DAY...

THEY NEED TO DRAG THEIR BUTTS INTO THE OFFICE IF THEY WANT TO KEEP THEIR JOBS.

Alex PEATTIE + TAYLOR

WE'VE COME UP WITH LOTS OF BUSINESS IDEAS WHICH WE PLAN TO PITCH TO POTENTIAL CLIENTS.

BUT WHY WOULD A CLIENT GO FOR AN IDEA FROM A SMALL BOUTIQUE LIKE OURS WHEN THEY'RE ALSO BEING PITCHED STUFF BY THE TEAMS FROM THE BIG INVESTMENT BANKS?

I MEAN, JUST THINK HOW VAST THE BANKS' BUDGETS ARE IN COMPARISON TO OURS. ALL THE EXTRA PEOPLE THEY CAN AFFORD TO EMPLOY.

YES...

MOST OF WHOM WORK IN COMPLIANCE, RISK MANAGEMENT, IN-HOUSE LEGAL, ESG ETC... BY THE TIME ALL OF THEM HAVE FINISHED APPROVING ANY BUSINESS IDEA, THE OPPORTUNITY WILL HAVE LONG PASSED.

YOU'RE RIGHT. WE CAN'T FAIL.

Alex FEATTIE + TAYLOR

SVB LATEST

PEOPLE ARE WONDERING IF THIS COULD BE A "NORTHERN ROCK MOMENT". REMEMBER THAT BANK THAT GOT IN TROUBLE IN 2007?

IMAGES SPREAD ON TV NEWS OF PEOPLE QUEUING OUTSIDE BRANCHES TO WITHDRAW MONEY, WHICH LED TO A RUN ON THE BANK AND ITS EVENTUAL COLLAPSE. IT WAS SEEN AS A HARBINGER OF THE GLOBAL FINANCIAL CRISIS A YEAR LATER.

OH, I DON'T THINK THAT'S A VALID PARALLEL, CLIVE. THAT WAS THE OLD DAYS. THE FINANCIAL WORLD IS MUCH MORE SOPHISTICATED TODAY.

WE NOW HAVE SOCIAL MEDIA - RUMOURS SPREAD IN MINUTES - AND ONLINE BANKING - PEOPLE CAN WITHDRAW THEIR MONEY INSTANTANEOUSLY... BANKS GO BUST A WHOLE LOT QUICKER...

THIS CRISIS WILL BE ON US BEFORE WE KNOW IT...

Alex FEATTIE + TAYLOR

WE FUND MANAGERS HAVE TO TAKE ALL SORTS OF ETHICAL CRITERIA INTO CONSIDERATION WHEN INVESTING IN COMPANIES THESE DAYS.

SURE, THERE'S A DETAILED CHECK-LIST TO BE FOLLOWED, BUT A COMPANY DOESN'T HAVE TO TICK EVERY BOX; JUST ENOUGH TO SATISFY US THAT IT'S A BUSINESS WE CAN JUSTIFY INVESTING OUR CLIENTS' MONEY IN.

NOW, THIS COMPANY THAT WE'RE LOOKING AT PERFORMS STRONGLY IN MOST AREAS: ESG POLICY - EXCELLENT; GENDER PAY GAP - LOW; FEMALE REPRESENTATION AT BOARD LEVEL - GOOD; DIVERSITY POLICY - SOUND; CORPORATE SOCIAL RESPONSIBILITY - GOOD.

RIGHT.

A SHAME IT DOESN'T ACTUALLY MAKE ANY MONEY...

WELL, WE DON'T ASK FOR PERFECTION...

Alex FEATTIE + TAYLOR

OUR BOSSES SEEM TO THINK THAT JUST BECAUSE THE TECH DEALS HAVE DRIED UP THAT THEY NO LONGER NEED US JUNIORS.

WE MAY BE YOUNG AND LACK EXPERIENCE, BUT TECH IS THE FUTURE OF OUR INDUSTRY AND WE'RE THE GENERATION THAT UNDERSTANDS IT AND HAS GROWN UP WITH IT.

WE ACCESS ALL OUR INFORMATION DIGITALLY AND ONLINE AND WE FIND IT INCOMPREHENSIBLE WHY OLDER PEOPLE STILL CHOOSE TO USE PHYSICAL HARD COPY DOCUMENTS.

LIKE THIS BUSINESS SCHOOL BROCHURE THAT SOMEONE'S LEFT ON MY DESK.

ON MINE TOO. THAT'S THE THIRD TIME THIS WEEK.

HOW ELSE CAN WE SUBTLY HINT TO THEM THAT THEY SHOULD RESIGN?

51

Alex PEATTIE + TAYLOR

SO YOU WORK FOR THAT SWISS BANK THAT'S JUST BEEN TAKEN OVER BY ITS MAJOR RIVAL?

YES...

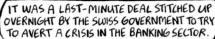

IT WAS A LAST-MINUTE DEAL STITCHED UP OVERNIGHT BY THE SWISS GOVERNMENT TO TRY TO AVERT A CRISIS IN THE BANKING SECTOR.

WELL, IT'S CREATED A BEHEMOTH OF A BANK WITH BIG OVERLAPS IN CAPACITY.

YOU SUDDENLY HAVE DOUBLE THE NUMBER OF PEOPLE IN ALL AREAS OF YOUR BANK'S OPERATION. IT CAN ONLY LEAD TO MASS REDUNDANCIES. YOU MUST BE FEARFUL FOR YOUR JOB..

NOT REALLY...

I WORK IN COMPLIANCE. I RECKON WE'LL BE TAKING ON EVEN <u>MORE</u> PEOPLE... TO IMPLEMENT ALL THE EXTRA-STRINGENT RULES THE REGULATORS NOW IMPOSE.

≡SIGH≡ YOUR BUSINESS ALWAYS DOES WELL OUT OF ANY CRISIS.

Alex PEATTIE + TAYLOR

SO YOU WORK IN COMPLIANCE AT THAT SWISS BANK THAT'S JUST BEEN TAKEN OVER AND YOU RECKON YOUR JOB IS SAFE?

YES

WELL, CLEARLY THERE WERE ALL SORTS OF INTRINSIC PROBLEMS WITH THE BANK THAT LED TO IT GETTING INTO SERIOUS TROUBLE, SO TO PREVENT A REOCCURRENCE OF THIS IT'S GOING TO BE NECESSARY TO INCREASE REGULATORY OVERSIGHT.

RIGHT...

WHICH MEANS I ANTICIPATE THAT WE'LL BE HIRING EVEN MORE COMPLIANCE OFFICERS TO DEAL WITH THE EXTRA WORKLOAD.

GREAT.

SO IF <u>I</u> DO MY JOB BADLY I GET FIRED; IF <u>YOU</u> DO YOURS BADLY YOU GET TO EXPAND YOUR DEPARTMENT...

WHO SAID LIFE WAS FAIR?

Alex PEATTIE + TAYLOR

WELL CENTRAL BANKS HELD THEIR NERVE AND HIKED INTEREST RATES TO COUNTER THE THREAT OF INFLATION...

YES.

OBVIOUSLY IT'S A RISKY STRATEGY THAT COULD LEAD TO FURTHER BANK FAILURES, LIKE THE SWISS BANK THAT JUST HAD TO BE RESCUED AT THE COST OF PROBABLY 40,000 JOBS...

TRUE, ALEX, BUT INFLATION IS ARGUABLY THE GREATEST DANGER.

WE'VE ALL BEEN FEELING THE ECONOMIC EFFECTS OF IT OF LATE. I MEAN, NAME ME ONE THING THAT'S GONE <u>DOWN</u> IN PRICE...

THE ASKING RATE FOR BANKERS... NOW THAT THE MARKET IS FLOODED WITH THEM.

WHICH IS HANDY FOR ME AS I'M HIRING FOR MY NEW FINANCIAL BOUTIQUE...

≡RING≡

THAT'S PROBABLY ANOTHER ONE CALLING NOW...

Alex — PEATTIE + TAYLOR

WHEN WE FIRST STARTED OUR FINANCIAL BOUTIQUE WE HAD A "NO D*CK-HEADS" POLICY, PLEDGING THAT WE'D ONLY WORK WITH PEOPLE THAT WE LIKED...

BUT THE REALITIES OF BRINGING IN BUSINESS MEANT THAT IT DIDN'T LAST AND I FIND MYSELF PITCHING TO FORMER CLIENTS OF MINE THAT I PERSONALLY DETEST.

LIKE THAT GUY WE JUST SAW?

YES. I'M CHARGING HIM EXTRA HIGH FEES TO COMPENSATE FOR HAVING TO WORK WITH HIM AGAIN.

WELL YOU PUT ON A GOOD FRONT OF BEING CHARMING. DOES HE HAVE ANY IDEA YOU HATE HIM?

I SUSPECT NOT...

OR HE'D HAVE NEGOTIATED EXTRA <u>LOW</u> FEES, REALISING WE MUST BE UTTERLY DESPERATE FOR BUSINESS IF WE'RE BOTHERING WITH <u>HIM</u>.

IT'S ALL SUCH A BLUFF...

Alex — PEATTIE + TAYLOR

I GUESS WE'VE BOTH BECOME EUROPHILES OVER RECENT YEARS, TONY

YES, YOU COULD SAY THAT

I VOTED FOR BREXIT, BUT SUBSEQUENT EVENTS HAVE MADE ME CHANGE MY MIND. THE UK LOSING ITS AUTOMATIC RIGHT TO CONDUCT BUSINESS IN EUROPE HAS BEEN A DISASTER...

SO NOW I'M IN FAVOUR OF HOLDING A SECOND REFERENDUM IN THE FERVENT HOPE THAT THE BRITISH ELECTORATE WILL SEE SENSE AND VOTE TO REJOIN THE E.U. IMMEDIATELY...

ME TOO.

IT'D GET US OUT OF THIS HELL-HOLE AND WE COULD GO BACK TO LONDON

I STILL CAN'T BELIEVE THE BANK MADE US COME AND WORK IN THIS TOKEN FRANKFURT OFFICE THAT IT SET UP POST-BREXIT...

Alex — PEATTIE + TAYLOR

HOW'S HONG KONG NOW THAT LOCKDOWN HAS BEEN LIFTED, BRIAN?

WHERE DO I BEGIN, ALEX?

A YEAR AGO THIS PLACE WAS A GHOST TOWN. YOU COULDN'T GO TO A BAR OR A RESTAURANT BECAUSE THEY WERE ALL CLOSED. YOU COULDN'T GET A HOTEL ROOM AS THEY'D ALL BEEN COMMANDEERED FOR QUARANTINE CASES...

YOU COULDN'T TAKE A TAXI AS THEY WERE BEING USED AS AMBULANCES, OR A PLANE AS FLIGHTS WERE BANNED. CONTRAST THAT WITH THE SITUATION <u>NOW</u>...

YOU CAN'T GET INTO ANY BARS OR RESTAURANTS BECAUSE THEY'RE ALL RAMMED. HOTEL ROOMS AND FLIGHTS ARE UNAVAILABLE BECAUSE THEY'RE ALL BOOKED OUT, AND YOU CAN'T GET A TAXI FOR LOVE OR MONEY...

AH, YES. EVERYONE'S THERE FOR THE HONG KONG 7s RUGBY.

53

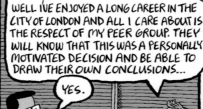

59

Alex PEATTIE + TAYLOR

ARE YOU LOOKING FORWARD TO THE BANK HOLIDAY WEEKEND TO MARK THE CORONATION?

I HAVE NO INTEREST IN SUCH THINGS, CLIVE.

ORDINARY PEOPLE HAVE BEEN DUPED BY THE ESTABLISHMENT INTO CELEBRATING WHAT IS LITTLE MORE THAN A REDUNDANT AND POINTLESS RELIC OF A BYGONE AGE...

EH?

WE'RE TALKING ABOUT A MORIBUND AND ANTIQUATED INSTITUTION THAT HAS LITTLE RELEVANCE TO OUR MODERN SOCIETY...

WHAT, THE MONARCHY?

ER, NO. THE BANK HOLIDAY... I MEAN, ANYONE OF ANY IMPORTANCE WORKS FROM HOME ON A MONDAY THESE DAYS, SO WE ALREADY GET THE DAY OFF...

Alex PEATTIE + TAYLOR

IT WAS NICE OF YOU TO TAKE ME ON THAT WEEKEND TRIP TO MIAMI, ALEX. AND EVEN NICER THAT YOU PAID FOR US TO FLY FIRST CLASS.

BUT, AS EVER, YOU BUMPED INTO SOMEONE YOU KNEW IN THE FIRST CLASS LOUNGE AND TALKED BUSINESS WITH HIM AND I FELT EXCLUDED

BUT PENNY HE'S THE CEO OF A MULTINATIONAL COMPANY...

IF I COULD GET HIM AS A CORPORATE CLIENT I COULD MAKE SOME FEES OUT OF HIM...

SO FOR YOU OUR ROMANTIC TRIP IS JUST A FINANCIAL OPPORTUNITY...

OKAY, I TAKE YOUR POINT, PENNY...

NOW THAT A MEETING WAS INVOLVED I CAN PUT THE COST OF MY TICKET THROUGH MY COMPANY AS A VALID BUSINESS EXPENSE...

DOUBLE RESULT!

Alex PEATTIE + TAYLOR

THERE'S THAT CEO WHO YOU WERE HOBNOBBING WITH IN THE LOUNGE AT MIAMI, ALEX...

OH YES.

THAT'S THE ADVANTAGE OF FLYING FIRST CLASS, PENNY. YOU MEET PEOPLE WHO COULD BE USEFUL TO YOU. I'VE HEARD THAT HIS COMPANY IS STRUGGLING IN THE ECONOMIC DOWNTURN AND THEY MIGHT BE LOOKING FOR NEW CORPORATE ADVISERS.

AND ME BUMPING INTO HIM INFORMALLY LIKE THIS MAY HAVE BOOSTED MY CHANCES OF PITCHING SUCCESSFULLY FOR HIS ACCOUNT.

BECAUSE YOU'VE MADE A PERSONAL CONNECTION WITH HIM?

ER, NO: BECAUSE I COULD ASK AWKWARD QUESTIONS AT HIS AGM NEXT WEEK ABOUT WHY HE WAS TRAVELLING FIRST CLASS WHEN HE'S JUST CUT HIS SHAREHOLDERS' DIVIDEND.

I SEE. SO IT'S BLACKMAIL AS USUAL THEN?

60

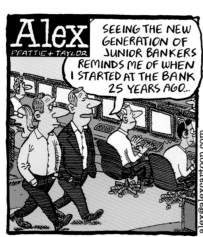

Alex PEATTIE + TAYLOR

IT MADE SENSE TO LOCATE OUR FINANCIAL BOUTIQUE IN MAYFAIR, LARGELY FOR THE BENEFIT OF THE WEALTH MANAGEMENT SIDE OF THE BUSINESS, WILLIAM.

MANY OF YOUR CLIENTS ARE FROM ABROAD AND EXTREMELY RICH, SO THEY'D EXPECT TO BE IN SURROUNDINGS THAT THEY'RE USED TO: A SMART OFFICE IN AN UPMARKET LOCATION.

BUT WHAT I HADN'T ANTICIPATED WAS THAT THEY MIGHT HAVE ATTITUDES WHICH ARE TOTALLY ALIEN AND RUN CONTRARY TO MY OWN VALUES AND ETHOS.

I KNOW WHAT YOU MEAN, ALEX.

THEY REQUIRE ABSOLUTE SECRECY AND DISCRETION.

SO I'M PAYING ALL THIS MONEY FOR A MAYFAIR ADDRESS AND I CAN'T EVEN HAVE A NAME-PLATE ON THE DOOR IN CASE SOMEONE SEES THEM COMING IN HERE?

SORRY, JUST A STREET NUMBER.

AT FIRST I HATED NOT BEING ABLE TO PUT A BRASS PLATE WITH MY NAME ON IT ON THE FRONT DOOR OF MY FINANCIAL BOUTIQUE.

MAYFAIR

BUT WE'RE PROVIDING LUCRATIVE WEALTH MANAGEMENT SERVICES TO SOME VERY AFFLUENT INDIVIDUALS, SO I HAVE TO BE MINDFUL OF THEIR PRIORITIES...

THERE ARE PEOPLE OUT THERE WHO THEY WOULDN'T WANT TO BE ABLE TO TRACK THEM AND TO KNOW WHERE THEY WERE AND WHAT THEIR BUSINESS MIGHT BE, AND I TOTALLY UNDERSTAND THAT...

BECAUSE NOW I FEEL THE SAME WAY MYSELF... IF I HAD A NAMEPLATE OUT THERE, EVERY FRIGGING PERSON I'VE EVER KNOWN IN THE CITY WOULD BE WALKING IN OFF THE STREET TRYING TO BLAG ME FOR A JOB...

YES, WE WOULDN'T WANT THAT...

MAYFAIR

Alex PEATTIE + TAYLOR

ALEX?! IS THAT YOU?! I HARDLY RECOGNISE YOU!

WELL, WITH US ARRANGING TO MEET UP AGAIN AFTER 40 YEARS ONE MUST EXPECT CHANGES...

TO BE HONEST I THOUGHT YOU WERE SOME SCRUFFY HOMELESS GUY FOR A MOMENT DRESSED LIKE THAT. NOT THE SUPER SUCCESSFUL VENTURE CAPITALIST I KNOW YOU'VE BECOME!

HA! RIGHT!

WELL, WE KNOW EACH OTHER FROM WAY BACK SO THERE'S NO NEED TO DRESS UP, SURELY? I CAN STILL WEAR MY COMFORTABLE HOODIE AND JEANS...

AND I STILL GET SAT AT THE BEST TABLE IN PRESTIGIOUS RESTAURANTS LIKE THIS ONE... THEN PEOPLE KNOW I'M REALLY RICH.

DAMMIT, YOU'RE DELIBERATELY MAKING ME LOOK LESS SUCCESSFUL THAN YOU ARE, AREN'T YOU? GRRR...

Panel 1: I STILL CAN'T BELIEVE THEY LET YOU INTO THIS EXCLUSIVE RESTAURANT LOOKING LIKE A HOBO, ANDY...

Panel 2: I EAT HERE ALL THE TIME, ALEX, AND THE STAFF KNOW BETTER THAN TO JUDGE DINERS BY APPEARANCES. THEY ARE AWARE THAT I AM A VERY SUCCESSFUL VENTURE CAPITALIST.

Panel 3: YOU ONLY HAVE TO LOOK AT THE EXTREMELY ATTENTIVE SERVICE THAT I AM RECEIVING FROM THE WAITER AND THE KEENNESS WITH WHICH HE'S TENDING TO MY EVERY REQUIREMENT.
YES...

Panel 4: HE KEEPS BRINGING US COMPLIMENTARY "AMUSE BOUCHES" BETWEEN COURSES... YOU MUST LOOK LIKE YOU NEED FREE STUFF...
I THINK YOU'LL FIND THAT THE REST OF THE MENU IS PRICED EXPENSIVELY ENOUGH TO ABSORB THE COST, ALEX.

Panel 5: THE STAFF KNOW YOU HERE SO WE GET USHERED TO THE BEST TABLE AND GIVEN SPECIAL TREATMENT EVEN THOUGH YOU'RE DRESSED DISREPUTABLY.

Panel 6: BUT YOU STILL LOOK LIKE A SCRUFF TO THE OTHER CUSTOMERS HERE...
YES, BUT WHEN THEY SEE ALL THE TOADYING AND SYCOPHANCY THEY DRAW THE CONCLUSION IT MUST BE SOMEONE RICH AND IMPORTANT WHO'S SITTING HERE.
TRUE.

Panel 7: BUT I'M NOT SURE IF YOU'RE CORRECT IF YOU THINK IT MAKES ANY OF THEM RESPECT YOU.

Panel 8: MORE LIKELY THEY RESPECT ME IN MY SUIT AND THINK I'M THE ONE BEING SUCKED UP TO AND I'M BUYING LUNCH FOR AN IMPOVERISHED FRIEND...
ONLY UNTIL THE MOMENT THEY SEE ME PICK UP THE TAB.
HUH? OVER MY DEAD BODY!
WAITER!
WAITER!

Panel 9: LOOK, ALEX, MAY I BE HONEST? WE AGREED TO MEET FOR LUNCH FOR OLD TIME'S SAKE BUT WHAT'S PAST IS PAST...

Panel 10: WE'VE SPENT AN HOUR MAKING POINTLESS SMALL TALK ABOUT OLD ACQUAINTANCES FROM BACK WHEN WE MOVED IN THE SAME CIRCLES.

Panel 11: BUT WE'RE NOT FRIENDS ANYMORE, AND WE'RE NOT GOING TO BE IN THE FUTURE EITHER. WE BELONG IN DIFFERENT WORLDS. WE DON'T EVEN KNOW ANY OF THE SAME PEOPLE.
I REALISE THAT NOW.

Panel 12: BUT I NEEDED TO BE SURE THAT NO-ONE WHO KNOWS ME WILL EVER BE TOLD THE EMBARRASSING STORY OF US MEETING UP AFTER 40 YEARS AND ME USING THE OCCASION TO PITCH WEALTH MANAGEMENT SERVICES TO YOU...
DAMN. I GAVE YOU THAT OPENING, DIDN'T I?
YUP.

Alex FEATTIE + TAYLOR

WHAT'S UP WITH THOSE TWO DINERS AT TABLE SIX?

THEY'RE FIGHTING OVER WHO GETS TO PAY THE BILL...

IT'S THE CLASSIC CLASH OF EGOS. THEY BOTH WANT TO SHOW THAT THEY'RE WEALTHY AND SUCCESSFUL AND NEITHER CAN BEAR TO ACCEPT CHARITY FROM THE OTHER. I NEED TO FIND A COMPROMISE SO THAT NEITHER LOSES FACE...

GENTLEMEN, IF I MAY MAKE A SUGGESTION? HOW ABOUT IF YOU TOSS A COIN TO DECIDE WHO PAYS?

A COIN?! DO YOU THINK I'D BOTHER WITH SUCH A LOW DENOMINATION OF MONEY? I DON'T CARRY SMALL CHANGE!

ME EITHER... I HAVEN'T EVEN SEEN A COIN SINCE THE 1990s.. UNLESS YOU COUNT BITCOIN..

WELL, LUCKILY I HAVE ONE. IS HONOUR SATISFIED NOW?

Alex FEATTIE + TAYLOR

DID THOSE TWO GENTLEMEN AT TABLE SIX SETTLE THEIR DISPUTE OVER WHO PAYS THE BILL?

YES, I GOT THEM TO TOSS A COIN FOR IT.

WELL, ALEX, I SUPPOSE I SHOULD THANK YOU FOR BUYING LUNCH, BUT YOU'VE REVEALED YOUR ULTERIOR MOTIVE IN WANTING TO CATCH UP WITH ME AGAIN AFTER ALL THESE YEARS...

YOU'D HEARD I WAS VERY RICH AND YOU WANTED TO PITCH YOUR FINANCIAL BOUTIQUE'S WEALTH MANAGEMENT SERVICES TO ME. WELL THAT TELLS ME WHAT SORT OF A PERSON YOU ARE...

A CHEAPSKATE. YOU'RE CLEARLY GOING TO PUT THIS THROUGH AS A BUSINESS EXPENSE...

NO, NO... WEALTH MANAGEMENT IS A SEPARATE DIVISION. I'M PAYING FOR THIS OUT OF MY OWN POCKET...

UH-OH... IT'S KICKING OFF AGAIN...

Alex FEATTIE + TAYLOR

HOW WAS YOUR LUNCH WITH YOUR OLD FRIEND, SIR?

NOT A GREAT SUCCESS, MARCEL.

IT SEEMS HE ONLY WANTED TO SEE ME AGAIN BECAUSE HE'D HEARD I'D BECOME RICH AND SUCCESSFUL, AND HE TRIED TO PITCH HIS FINANCIAL BOUTIQUE'S WEALTH MANAGEMENT SERVICES TO ME.

PLUS HE GOT TO PAY FOR THE MEAL, WHICH LEFT ME LOOKING AS IF I WAS POOR AND NEEDED A FAVOUR...

OH WELL, SIR, AT LEAST YOU WON'T HAVE TO SEE HIM AGAIN...

ON THE CONTRARY. I'M NOW SOCIALLY OBLIGATED TO INVITE HIM OUT FOR ANOTHER LUNCH, WHICH I'LL PAY FOR IN ORDER TO AVOID BEING NOMINALLY IN HIS DEBT...

ETIQUETTE TRUMPS ENMITY..

Alex PEATTIE + TAYLOR

I'VE BEEN PHONING ROUND MY OLD CONTACTS IN THE CITY TO TRY TO SOURCE BUSINESS FOR OUR FINANCIAL BOUTIQUE.

OF COURSE MANY OF THEM HAVE RETIRED AND SO NO LONGER WORK FOR COMPANIES THAT COULD BECOME OUR CLIENTS, IN WHICH CASE I CAN REFER THEM TO YOU AS OUR IN-HOUSE WEALTH MANAGER, WILLIAM.

RIGHT, SO IT'S WIN-WIN FOR US...

OF COURSE FOR REGULATORY REASONS WE HAVE TO KEEP A STRICT CHINESE WALL BETWEEN OUR TWO SIDES OF THE OPERATION.

ABSOLUTELY, ALEX.

YOU WOULDN'T WANT TO KNOW HOW MUCH MONEY SOME OF YOUR OLD FRIENDS HAVE MADE.

NOT WHILE I'M STILL HAVING TO WORK, NO...

SO IT'S GOOD THAT YOU CAN'T TELL ME.

Alex PEATTIE + TAYLOR

SO YOU DON'T MIND THAT THE BANK IS RELOCATING YOU TO OUR PARIS OFFICE?

ON THE CONTRARY. I'M DELIGHTED...

PARIS IS COMING TO RIVAL LONDON AS THE FINANCIAL CENTRE OF EUROPE. AND THOUGH BEING SENT TO WORK IN FRANKFURT CAN BE SEEN AS A DEMOTION OR AN INVITATION TO RESIGN, PARIS IS A DIFFERENT MATTER.

YOU CAN EASILY IMAGINE WHAT BEING BASED IN THE CAPITAL CITY OF FRANCE HAS TO OFFER...

OPERA, THEATRE, A VIBRANT CULTURE AND CUISINE?

ACTUALLY I WAS THINKING OF THE SUPER-STRICT FRENCH EMPLOYMENT LAWS. IT'S VERY HARD TO FIRE ANYONE THERE. SO ME BEING RELOCATED MEANS THAT MY JOB MUST BE SAFE.

BUT WHAT ABOUT MINE HERE IN LONDON..? OH GOD...

Alex PEATTIE + TAYLOR

I WAS IN THE CITY TODAY AND I BUMPED INTO AN OLD CLIENT OF MINE.

WE HAD A CHAT AND I OFFERED TO BUY HIM LUNCH SOMETIME TO DISCUSS BUSINESS. I CAN'T REALLY AFFORD IT BUT I'M HOPING HE MIGHT HELP ME FIND A JOB...

DID YOU ADMIT TO HIM THAT YOU'RE CURRENTLY UNEMPLOYED?

WHAT, AND THAT I ONLY GO INTO THE CITY THESE DAYS IN THE HOPE OF MEETING PEOPLE WHO COULD BE USEFUL TO ME? ER, NO...

DID YOU ADMIT TO CLIVE THAT YOU'RE RETIRED AND YOU ONLY GO INTO THE CITY THESE DAYS TO GET YOUR HAIR CUT BECAUSE YOU NEVER GOT ROUND TO CHANGING YOUR BARBER?

ER, NO. I QUITE FANCIED A FREE LUNCH...

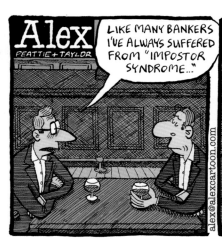

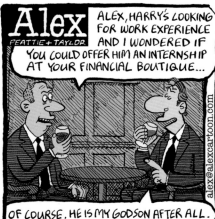

YOUR DAD HAS ASKED ME TO CONSIDER YOU FOR AN INTERNSHIP IN MY FINANCIAL BOUTIQUE, HARRY.

IT SEEMS FAIR ENOUGH, HE IS AN OLD FRIEND AND A LONG-STANDING CLIENT OF MINE AND YOU'RE MY GODSON: BUT DON'T THINK I'D BE OFFERING YOU A JOB PURELY OUT OF CHARITY.

BEFORE I DO SO I'LL NEED TO ASK YOU SOME PRETTY SEARCHING QUESTIONS: ABOUT CAREER PLANS, LONG-TERM OBJECTIVES, DEGREE OF COMMITMENT, AMBITIONS AND ASPIRATIONS.

OF COURSE, ALEX.

RIGHT. SO HOW LONG IS YOUR DAD INTENDING TO KEEP WORKING FOR? DOES HE HAVE ANY PLANS TO RETIRE SOON?

I DON'T WANT TO WASTE A DESK ON YOU IF HE'S NOT GOING TO BE AROUND TO GIVE ME ANY BUSINESS IN RETURN...

ALEX, I THINK YOU NEED TO MOVE QUICKLY IF YOU ARE GOING TO OFFER ME A JOB IN YOUR FINANCIAL BOUTIQUE...

WHY'S THAT, CLIVE?

ONCE WORD GETS OUT THAT I'M AVAILABLE I'M BOUND TO GET LOADS OF OFFERS. PLUS I HAVE KNOWLEDGE OF FINANCIAL MARKETS, WHICH YOU'LL WANT TO AVAIL YOURSELF OF WHILE IT'S STILL CURRENT

WHAT I'M SAYING IS THAT YOU NEED TO BEAR IN MIND WHAT SOMEONE LIKE ME WHO'S RECENTLY WORKED FOR A MAJOR INVESTMENT BANK CAN BRING TO YOUR START-UP.

OH YES...

A FREE BLOOMBERG SCREEN, WHICH BLOOMBERG OFFERS TO NEWLY-REDUNDANT PEOPLE FOR 3 MONTHS. I COULD USE HAVING ANOTHER ONE OF THOSE IN THE OFFICE...

THEY'RE SO EXPENSIVE...

APPARENTLY AI CAN NOW HELP EXECUTIVES LIKE US TO MANAGE ONE OF THE BANES OF OUR LIVES: EMAIL.

WE RECEIVE LITERALLY HUNDREDS OF EMAILS A DAY, WHICH WITH OUR HECTIC SCHEDULE WE'VE NO TIME TO DEAL WITH. BUT NOW YOU CAN GET A CHATBOT TO DO IT FOR YOU.

NOT ONLY CAN IT READ AND SUMMARISE YOUR EMAILS FOR YOU, IT CAN EVEN REPLY TO THEM ON YOUR BEHALF...

HMM. THAT SEEMS VERY DANGEROUS...

EVERYONE KNOWS IF YOU REPLY TO AN EMAIL YOU JUST RECEIVE ANOTHER ONE IN RETURN.

YES. WHICH THESE DAYS WOULD LIKELY ALSO BE WRITTEN BY A BOT...

AND YOUR INBOX WOULD END UP BEING EVEN MORE OVERWHELMED THAN IT WAS BEFORE.

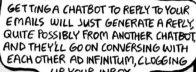

73

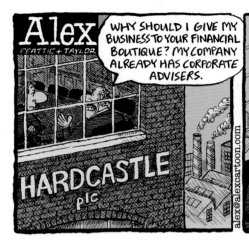

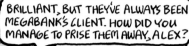

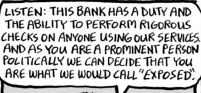

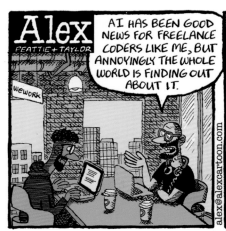

78

Alex FEATTIE+TAYLOR

WHENEVER THERE'S A WEATHER-RELATED DISASTER SOMEWHERE PEOPLE LIKE YOU ARE ALWAYS QUICK TO BLAME CLIMATE CHANGE, BUT THAT'S MISLEADING...

WHAT WE'RE ACTUALLY WITNESSING HERE ARE QUITE MUNDANE EVENTS BROUGHT ABOUT DURING VARIATIONS OF ORDINARY WEATHER PATTERNS.

YOU CAN'T SEEM TO ACCEPT THAT THIS IS _NOT_ UNEXPECTED, IT'S _NOT_ A CATASTROPHE, IT'S _NOT_ A DISASTER. IT'S JUST _NORMAL_...

AUSTRALIA _NORMALLY_ BEATS ENGLAND IN THE CRICKET ANYWAY AND IT _ALWAYS_ RAINS IN THE SUMMER IN THIS COUNTRY.

NO! IT'S FREAKISH BAD LUCK CAUSED BY GLOBAL WARMING. WE'D HAVE WON OTHERWISE.

STOP MAKING EXCUSES, POM.

Alex FEATTIE+TAYLOR

WORRYINGLY, CHINESE PROPERTY COMPANIES SEEM TO BE FAILING AT THE MOMENT. I HOPE THE AUTHORITIES CAN STOP IT GETTING WORSE...

ROYAL CHINA HOTEL HONG KONG

THEIR ECONOMY TOOK A BATTERING IN THE PANDEMIC...

WE ALL REMEMBER DURING COVID SEEING PICTURES ON TV OF THE STREETS DESERTED DUE TO LOCKDOWN, SHOPS AND PUBLIC SPACES EMPTY OF PEOPLE, BUSINESS ACTIVITY NON-EXISTENT...

YEH. NIGHTMARE!

LET'S PRAY WE NEVER SEE THAT AGAIN.

YES.

NOT ON TELLY ANYWAY. THEY NEED TO BAN JOURNALISTS FROM GOING INTO ANY OF THOSE GHOST CITIES WHICH GOT BUILT AS INVESTMENT PROPERTIES BUT NO ONE WANTS TO LIVE IN...

IMPUDENT FOREIGNER! STOP SPREADING LIES!

OOPS

I _TOLD_ YOU NOT TO TAKE YOUR PHONE OVER THERE ON BUSINESS...

Alex FEATTIE+TAYLOR

FOOD PRICE INFLATION HAS BEEN COMPLETELY OUT OF CONTROL OVER THE LAST YEAR OR SO...

IT'S DUE TO VARIOUS FACTORS: CLIMATE CHANGE CAUSING HARVEST FAILURES, DISRUPTION TO SUPPLY CHAINS FROM THE WAR IN UKRAINE, BREXIT, THE WEAKNESS OF STERLING ETC ETC...

AND OF COURSE WE ALL KNOW THAT ANY INCREASE IN THE PRICE OF BASIC FOODSTUFFS ENDS UP BEING PASSED ON TO THE END USER WHICH IS PEOPLE LIKE YOU AND ME...

THAT'S A DISAGREEABLE THOUGHT...

I LIKE TO THINK THAT THE HIGH PRICES HERE REFLECT THE EXCLUSIVITY AND SOPHISTICATION OF THE DINING EXPERIENCE THAT WE'RE ABOUT TO HAVE...

QUITE AND NOTHING TO DO WITH ANYTHING AS VULGAR AS THE COST OF THE RAW MATERIALS. LE GOURMET

Also available from Masterley Publishing

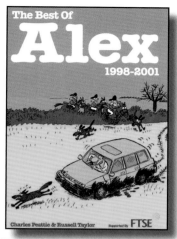

The Best of Alex 1998 - 2001
Boom to bust via the dotcom bubble.

The Best of Alex 2002
Scandals rock the corporate world.

The Best of Alex 2003
Alex gets made redundant.

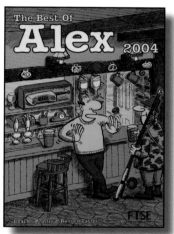

The Best of Alex 2004
And gets his job back.

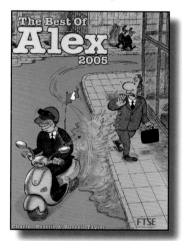

The Best of Alex 2005
Alex has problems with the French.

The Best of Alex 2006
Alex gets a new American boss.

The Best of Alex 2007
Alex restructures Christmas.

The Best of Alex 2008
The credit crunch bites

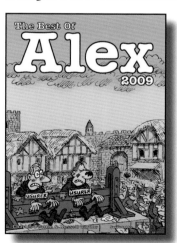

The Best of Alex 2009
Global capitalism self-destructs.

The Best of Alex 2010
Somehow the City lurches on.

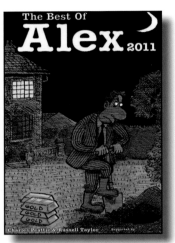

The Best of Alex 2011
The financial crisis continues.

The Best of Alex 2012
The Olympics come to London.

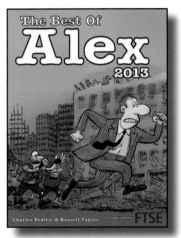

The Best of Alex 2013
It's a wonderful crisis.

The Best of Alex 2014
The 'New Normal' takes hold.

The Best of Alex 2015
Compliance rules the roost.

The Best of Alex 2016
Alex battles Brexit and Bitcoin.

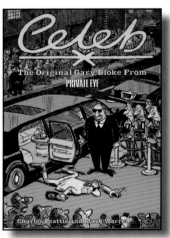

Celeb
Wrinkly rock star Gary Bloke.

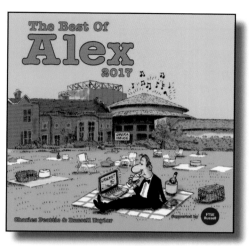

The Best of Alex 2017
30 years in the City and counting...

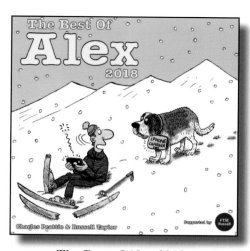

The Best of Alex 2018
Brexit and more Brexit...

The Best of Alex 2019
And even more Brexit...

The Best of Alex 2020
Covid comes to call.

The Best of Alex 2021
Working from home.

The Best of Alex 2022
War, inflation and a tech crash.

All books available from www.alexcartoon.com

For further details on prices and delivery charges for books, cartoons or merchandise please contact:
Email: alex@alexcartoon.com / **X:** @alexmasterley

**You can purchase a print of any cartoon featured in this book to display in your home or office.
They measure 4 x 14 inches. All prints are signed by the creators and are available from the Alex website.**

Alex original artwork is exclusively available from

Chris Beetles Gallery

8 & 10 Ryder Street, St James's, London SW1Y 62B.

Web: www.chrisbeetles.com

Email: gallery@chrisbeetles.com / Phone: 020 7839 7551